For Anz Johansen

With special thanks to David DuChene, Ziad Amrah, Jamie Johansen, Kristin Johnson, Trish Cruze, Jeff Harrison, Jacci Krebsbach, Florence Knaak, and, of course, my family.

Monsters
Make Me
Giggle

Monster Album

Choose one of the monsters here. Then go to the page with the same number to see the whole picture!

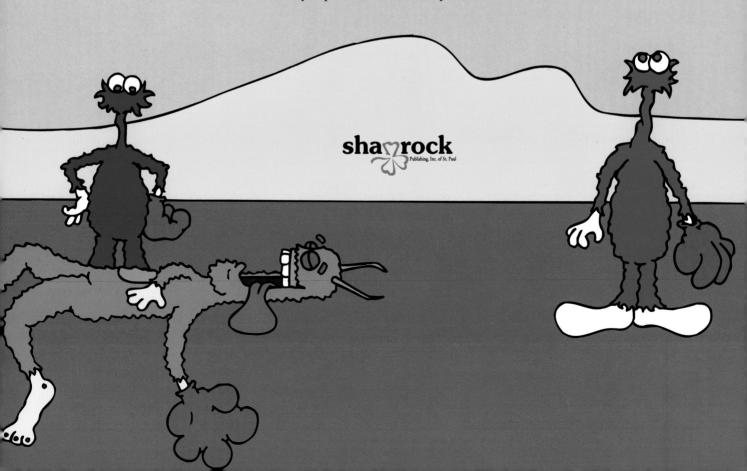

shamrock
Publishing, Inc. of St. Paul

Monsters
Make Me
Giggle

Written and Illustrated by Joel Fashingbauer

There are monsters
who are **big**

and others
who are small.

These monsters are fat.

Some monsters have horns and great big feet.

Others just love
to eat
and eat
and eat.

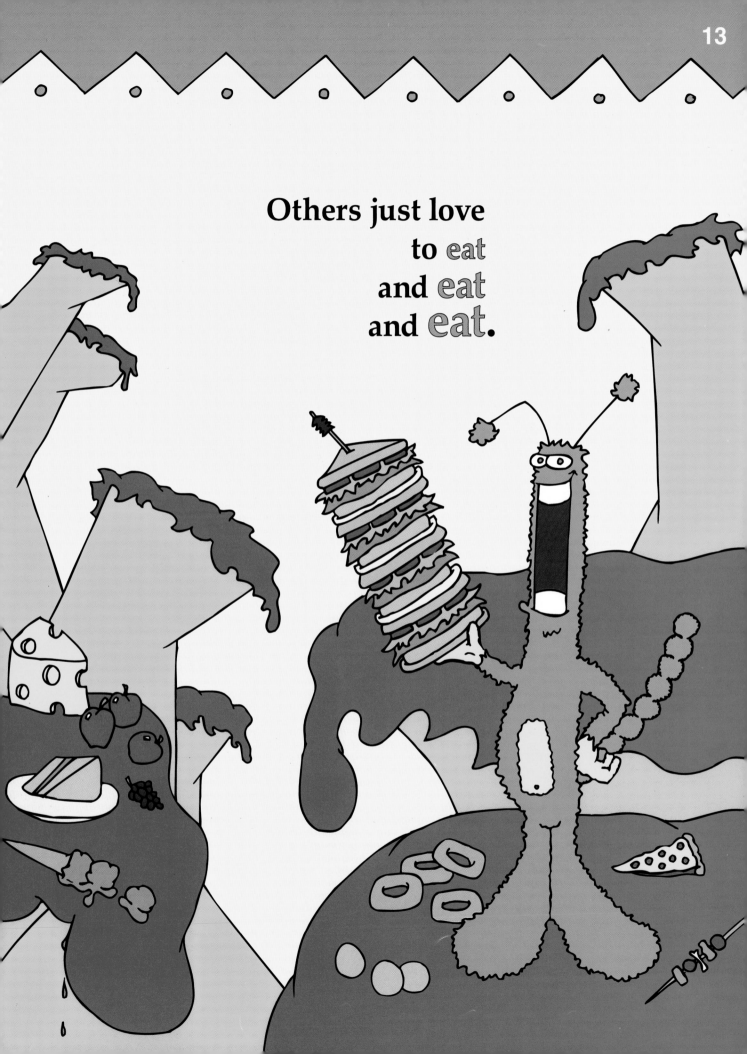

There are monsters with one head,
others have two,

some have polka dots...

...and these are blue.

This monster has fur
and is very, very hairy.

This lucky monster
has a pet canary.

There are monsters
who are girls,

and some
who are boys...

...this monster has fun
playing with toys.

Some monsters have
healthy teeth
and nice, pretty smiles.

Others can fly,
and see for miles and miles.

This monster is **busy** and loves to **play**...

When you look at these monsters,
you will surely see,

there are some just like you,
and some just like me.

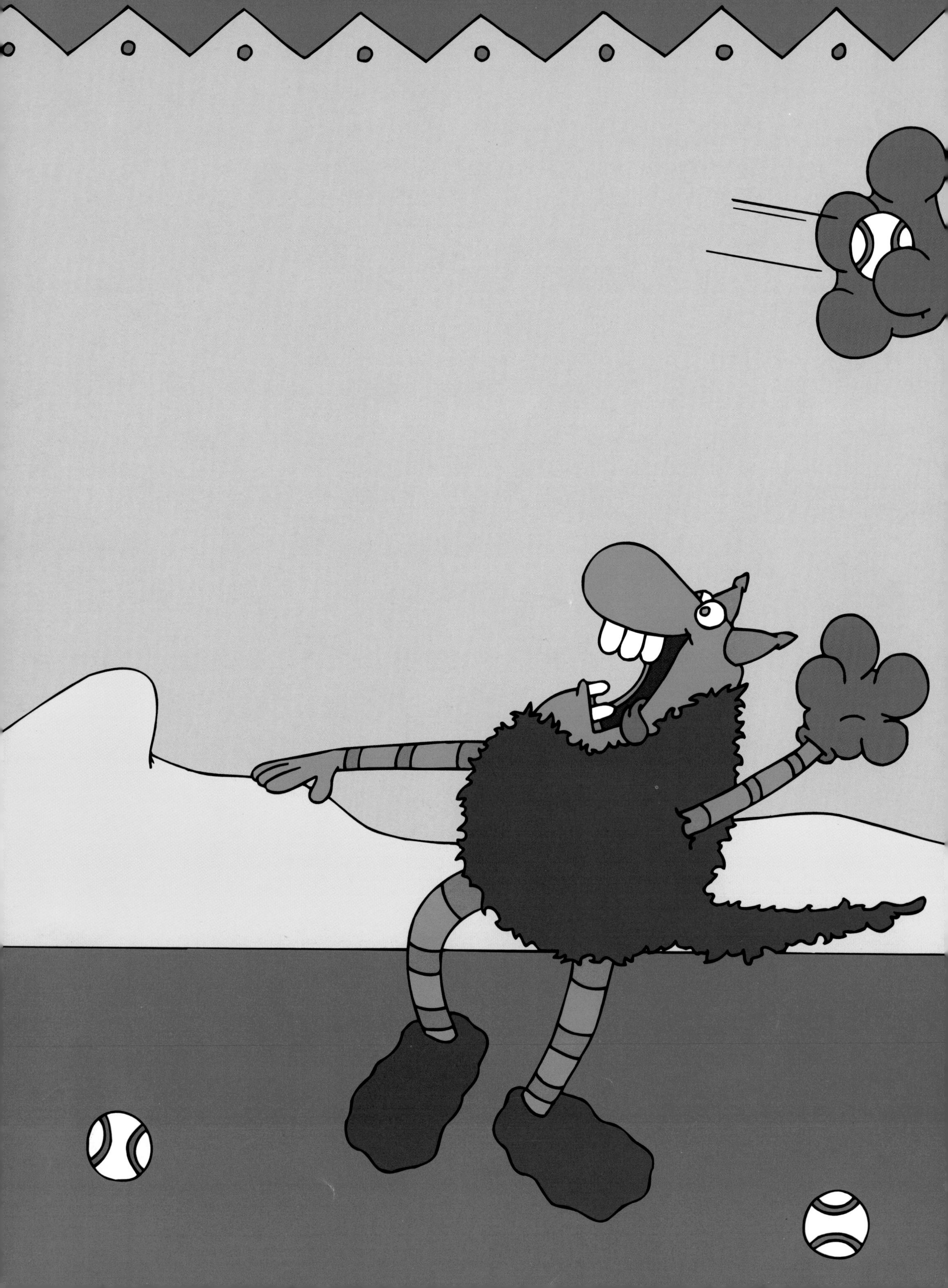

About the Author

Joel Fashingbauer was born in Shoreview, Minnesota, and began drawing at age seven. As a child, he secretly kept three little monsters in the coffee can under his bed. His love of creating strange, humorous characters developed while he was studying for his B.A. in Psychology at the University of Minnesota.

Joel's future includes graduate school, a comic strip, more books, and stand-up comedy. He currently lives in Minneapolis, and it is said his monsters follow him wherever he goes.